On loan from the School Libraries Resources Service.
Please return by the end of the current term.
Telephone: 020 8359 3931   Fax: 020 8201 3018
Email: slrs@barnet.gov.uk

www.libraries.barnet.gov.uk

BARNET
LONDON BOROUGH

D0773925

Britain's castles and battlefields are an exciting and fascinating part of our national heritage. Whether grand or simple, magnificent or ruined, every castle has its tales to tell and by visiting them we can learn about our past and the people who once lived there.

The word 'castle' entered the English language just before the Norman Conquest of 1066: it described a circular mound with a wooden palisade on the summit, surrounded by a dry ditch. The Normans were great castle builders, their own early wooden structures and those of the Anglo-Saxons, were soon replaced by stone. The Crusades allowed European military engineers to study the sophisticated fortresses of the Byzantine (Eastern Roman) Empire. This new knowledge from the East revolutionised castle building. More and more elaborate features were added (see pages 6/7) until the technology of the cannon made the castle obsolete. The British Isles has a bloody history, not only as an imperial power overseas but in its own backyard, usually spurred by struggles for power and succession to the throne. The Civil War saw Englishmen fighting Englishmen that led to the destruction of many castles and some of the bloodiest battles ever witnessed on British soil.

Discover the past and learn the stories of the castles and battles that are all around the British Isles. This I-Spy book may help you understand how we evolved into the Britain of today.

How to use your I-SPY book

You need 1000 points to send off for your I-Spy badge (see p64) but that is not too difficult because there are masses of points in every book. As you make each I-Spy, write your score in the box.

2

WHAT IS A CASTLE?

Most castles, as we think of them now, were built during the Middle Ages. At the height of the castle building era between 1066 and 1650, the British Isles had over 2,000 castles. Unlike other buildings, such as a church or a place of work, the medieval stone castle served more than one purpose. They were designed and built to hold down conquered territory, demonstrating the power and wealth of the owner. Castles were principally the private residence of the owner and his family but were built strong enough to defend its occupants whilst acting as a base from which attacks could be launched. A castle is, in short, a properly fortified military residence. Later castles served only a single purpose – forts for defence or stately homes for residence. Many castles occupy the highest point in the area, the natural terrain acting as a further aid to defence.

Bamburgh Castle (Northumberland)

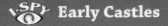
MOTTE AND BAILEY CASTLES

The earliest examples of castles came in a variety of configurations but the most common was a single mound (motte) and enclosure (bailey). Most mottes were constructed by digging a deep ditch and heaping up the remaining soil. The ditch was sometimes filled with water – introducing the moat. The combination of mud and water provided good obstacles. The motte and bailey design was the standard defence of the 11th and 12th centuries. The biggest disadvantage of this type of castle was its vulnerability. Wood both rots and burns. The shell keep (stone), a much larger structure, on a lower motte, into which most of the accommodation could be fitted became more common in the 12th century.

Castle Wiston, Wales

Later, many of the wooden towers were replaced by stone keeps. One of the earliest, if not the earliest example is Colchester Castle, Essex. The need for a stronger and more permanent medium had come and the introduction of the stone castle began with the Norman invasion of 1066. By the late 11th century there were approximately 100 well defended castles in England. The largest of these early castles still survives in Wiltshire - Old Sarum.

Old Sarum, Wiltshire

Colchester Castle

😊 I-SPY Tick List:

• **Motte and Bailey Castle**	40 ◯
• **Old Sarum**	25 ◯
• **Colchester Castle**	25 ◯

I-SPY A Medieval Castle

In the illustration below you will find all the key elements of a typical medieval castle. Explanations and descriptions of these can be found pages 8 to 15.

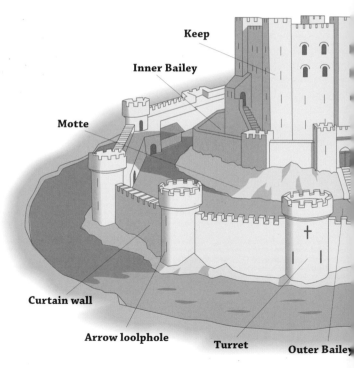

Keep

Inner Bailey

Motte

Curtain wall

Arrow loolphole

Turret

Outer Bailey

A Medieval Castle

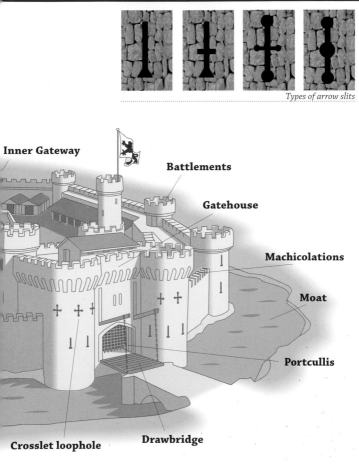

Types of arrow slits

Inner Gateway

Battlements

Gatehouse

Machicolations

Moat

Portcullis

Crosslet loophole

Drawbridge

MOAT

The moat was a deep, wide ditch surrounding a castle as a protection against assault. It may have even gone around the whole town! A castle moat filled with water would have been difficult to cross and it also reduced the risk of tunnelling – one of the most serious forms of attack was to undermine part of a castle. Not all castles were built near a water supply and sometimes the moat would have been filled with pointed wooden stakes.

I-SPY points: 15

Date:

Cardiff Castle moat

Hever Castle moat

DUNGEON

The word dungeon conjurers up all sorts of horrors and castle dungeons were often dark, lonely cells located in an underground room of one of the towers. They were used as a more severe place of punishment than a jail, and in extreme cases used for torturing prisoners.

I-SPY points: 20

Date: _____

Warwick Castle dungeon

Edinburgh Castle dungeon

MURDER HOLES

Murder holes were holes made in the ceilings of passages or entranceways through which heavy missiles or dangerous substances could be thrown on the enemy. Missiles included heavy stones, boiling water and boiling tar or pitch. During an attack any rotting materials such as dung or even dead bodies could be dropped!

I-SPY points: 25

Date: _____

Edinburgh Castle Great Hall

Dover Castle Great Hall

GREAT HALL

The life of the medieval castle revolved around the Great Hall. It was the main meeting and dining area and used by everyone who lived in the castle.

Entertainment was a major feature of castle life with music, acrobats and jesters. Sweet smelling herbs such as lavender, camomile and rose petals were scattered to disguise the bad smells of the castles which were prevalent due to the inadequate plumbing and drainage systems!

I-SPY points: 15

Date: _____

Sterling Castle Great Hall

DRAWBRIDGE

The drawbridge was a heavy timber platform that crossed the moat and allowed entry to the castle. It could be raised and lowered from inside the castle when required.

I-SPY points: 15
Date:

Hever Castle drawbridge

BARBICAN

The Barbican was an exterior walled defensive passage with a portcullis and multiple gates leading to the main entrance of the castle – the Gatehouse.

I-SPY points: 25
Date:

Walmgate Barbican, York

PORTCULLIS

The Portcullis was a heavy iron or wooden grilled door that was suspended from the Barbican or gatehouse ceiling. It was rapidly dropped down if the castle came under attack.

I-SPY points: 20
Date: _____

Carlisle Castle portcullis

CRENULATIONS

Crenulations, or Battlements, were situated on the top of castle towers and walls and provided a fighting platform and good vantage point from which soldiers launched arrows, then hid behind.

I-SPY points: 15
Date: _____

13

MOTTE

The Motte was a man-made mound of earth on which a Norman tower was built. It was surrounded by a ditch and a courtyard, containing other buildings, called a Bailey.

Yelden Castle, Bedfordshire

BAILEY

The Bailey was a defended yard which contained barracks, stables, livestock and other buildings for storing food, weapons and equipment. The entrance to the Bailey was through a large wooden gate. Some Bailey gates had Guardhouses built either side.

I-SPY points: 25

Date:

I-SPY points: 25

Date:

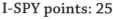

Caernarfon Castle

14

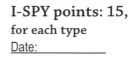

ARROW LOOPHOLES

Castles were built with arrow slits or loopholes in many parts of the buildings, at all levels. These openings were designed to allow archers inside the castle room to shoot at invaders or attackers in relative safety. The narrow slits, usually vertical, were tapered inwards to give the archer the greatest room to shoot without fear of being shot himself. Arrow slits came in a variety of shapes and sizes. Some of these are illustrated below and on page 7.

I-SPY points: 15, for each type

Date: _____

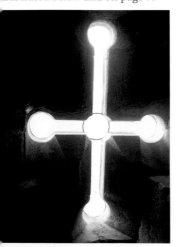

The King of the Castle

Edward I (1239-1307) instigated a remarkable period of castle building in Wales in the years 1277-84.

This mighty undertaking had a military motive – to enforce English rule over the Welsh. His devastating campaigns led to the building of massive castles to dominate the territory. The concentrated building process was unique to his reign. The task was enormous by any standards, involving huge work forces, materials and ultimately money. In total, ten castles were built: Aberystwyth, Beaumaris, Builth, Caernarfon, Conwy, Flint, Harlech, Hope, Rhuddlan and Ruthin. Work was also undertaken at Chirk, Denbigh, Hawarden and Holt.

😊 I-SPY Tick List:

• **Aberystwyth**	25	◯
• **Beaumaris**	25	◯
• **Builth**	25	◯
• **Caernarfon**	25	◯
• **Conwy**	25	◯
• **Flint**	25	◯
• **Harlech**	25	◯
• **Hope**	25	◯
• **Rhuddlan**	25	◯
• **Ruthin**	25	◯

Flint Castle

Caernarfon Castle

To oversee this campaign, he entrusted the work to the country's leading castle-builder, Master Mason James Savoyard of St. George. Starting with Rhuddlan he oversaw the construction process, culminating with Beaumaris, by which time he had perfected the design of a castle with concentric walls, where the outer wall is lower than the inner allowing better defence.

😊 I-SPY Tick List:

• **Chirk**	35	◯
• **Denbigh**	35	◯
• **Hawarden**	35	◯
• **Holt**	35	◯

Aberystwyth Castle

Beaumaris Castle

Most castles have been altered or rebuilt during their lifetime. Some survive virtually intact; others have suffered the ravages of war and time less well. Here are some examples of the most well-known.

EDINBURGH CASTLE

Perched high on its volcanic rock, the castle dominates the City skyline. For centuries the home of Scottish kings and queens, its various styles tell of changing uses, from siege (defence) to attack.

I-SPY points: 20

Date: _____

WARWICK CASTLE

Warwick Castle was built by William the Conqueror in 1068 and is today a theme-park where you can experience jousting knights, medieval banquets and falconry, alongside the 1900s water-wheel electricity generator.

I-SPY points: 15

Date: _____

Featured Castles I-SPY

DOVER CASTLE

Built by Henry II in the 1180s, the castle played a huge part in WWI. The Dunkirk evacuation was planned from the Secret Wartime Tunnels. The Great Tower has been completely restored how it would have looked in the 12th century.

I-SPY points: 15
Date: _____

BODIAM CASTLE

Bodiam Castle is a perfect example of a late medieval moated castle. Built around 1385 its defences were never severely tested but its condition deteriorated until the early 20th century when it was restored to its original condition by the then owner, Lord Curzon. *(Robertsbridge, East Sussex)*

I-SPY points: 15
Date: _____

WINDSOR CASTLE

Originally built by William the Conqueror after the Norman Conquest in 1066, this is the world's oldest and largest inhabited castle. Queen Elizabeth II's official residence has sumptuous state apartments. English monarchs buried in St George's chapel include Henry VIII.

I-SPY points: 10
Date: _____

CARLISLE CASTLE

The castle is over 900 years old and has been the scene of many historical episodes in British history. Given the proximity of Carlisle to the border between England and Scotland, it has been the centre of many wars and invasions.

I-SPY points: 15
Date: _____

CASTLE HOWARD

One of the grandest private residences in Britain, most of it was built between 1699 and 1712 for the 3rd Earl of Carlisle, It is not a true castle (see page 3): It is a prime example of an English country house constructed after the main castle-building era, never intended for a military function. Castle Howard was used as the location for the TV series and film, *Brideshead Revisited. (Near York)*

I-SPY points: 20

Date:

LINCOLN CASTLE

Lincoln Castle was constructed during the late 11th century by William the Conqueror on the site of a pre-existing Roman fortress. It remained in use as a prison and law court into modern times, and is one of the better preserved castles. It is still possible to walk around the immense 12th-century walls.

It is also home to one of the four surviving originals of the Magna Carta, sealed by King John after his meeting with the Barons at Runnymede in 1215.

I-SPY points: 20,
double for Magna Carta

Date:

LEEDS CASTLE

Leeds Castle, in Kent, dates back to 1119, though a manor house stood on the same site from the ninth century. The castle is mostly a 19th century rebuilding or restoration.

I-SPY points: 15

Date: _____

ARUNDEL CASTLE

Arundel Castle is a restored medieval castle. The castle dates from the reign of Edward the Confessor (1042-1066) and was completed by Roger de Montgomery, who became the first to hold the earldom of Arundel by the grace of William the Conqueror. The castle was damaged in the English Civil War and restored in the 18th and 19th centuries.

I-SPY points: 20

Date: _____

ALNWICK CASTLE

Alnwick Castle is a castle and stately home in Alnwick, Northumberland, England and the residence of the Duke of Northumberland, built immediately following the Norman Conquest, and renovated and remodelled a number of times.

The castle is used for the exterior and interior of Hogwarts in the *Harry Potter* films.

I-SPY points: 20
Date: _____

HEVER CASTLE

Hever Castle was the childhood home of Anne Boleyn, Henry VIII's second wife. Henry bestowed it on Anne of Cleves upon the annulment of their marriage. Today it is an extremely popular restored country house.

I-SPY points: 15
Date: _____

ROCHESTER CASTLE

Rochester Castle is one of the best-preserved castles of its kind in the UK. There has been a fortification on this site since Roman times (c AD43), though it is the keep of 1127 and the Norman castle which can be seen today.

I-SPY points: 20
Date: _____

CAERNARFON CASTLE

Caernarfon Castle is one of the most impressive of the castles built by Edward I (see page 16-17) and is one of Europe's greatest medieval fortresses.

Begun in 1283 Caernarfon was constructed not only as a military stronghold but also as a seat of government and royal palace. Edward I took the title of Prince of Wales from the Welsh. Since that time, the eldest son of the King or Queen of England has been known as the Prince of Wales. In 1969, during a ceremony at Caernarfon, Prince Charles was invested the 21st Prince of Wales by his mother, Queen Elizabeth II.

I-SPY points: 25
Date: _____

TOWER OF LONDON

The Tower of London is often identified with the White Tower, the original fortress built by William the Conqueror in 1078. However, the tower as a whole is a complex of several buildings set within two concentric rings of defensive walls and a moat.

The tower's primary function was as a fortress, a royal palace and a prison but it has also served as a place of execution and torture, an armoury, a treasury, a zoo, the Royal Mint, a public records office, an observatory and since 1303, the home of the Crown Jewels.

I-SPY points: 15

Date: _____

THE END OF CASTLES

Once-splendid castles were subject to sieges and cannon bombardment that caused massive damage during the Civil Wars (see page 49-51). Many castles were abandoned and the stone used for building local houses. Castles that survived were mainly those held by the Parliamentary troops, which explains why Windsor and Dover Castles retain so much of their original architecture. Plundering castles for demolition materials continued right up to the 18th century when attitudes began to change. A growing sense of responsibility toward physical remains of the past led to the passing of the Ancient Monuments Act in 1882.

I-SPY points: 25,

for any ruined castle

Date: _____

Ludlow Castle (Shropshire)

Goodrich Castle (Herefordshire)

KENILWORTH CASTLE

Kenilworth is one of the largest castle ruins in England. At the end of the Civil War it was deliberately damaged to prevent it being used as a Royalist stronghold. (Warwickshire)

I-SPY points: 25

Date:

RESTORMEL CASTLE

Restormel has been called 'the finest unaltered example of a Norman shell keep in England'. Built around 1100, it fell into ruins after the Civil War. (Cornwall)

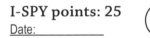

I-SPY points: 25

Date:

CORFE CASTLE

Corfe started as a motte castle in the 1080s and was to become one the strongest in all England. It was damaged by explosives and undermining on the orders of Parliament in 1646, at the end of the civil war. *(Dorset)*

I-SPY points: 25

Date: _____

TINTAGEL CASTLE

Tintagel Castle was built 800 years ago by the Earl of Cornwall, brother of the King of England. The Earl was intrigued by the legends of King Arthur, the magician Merlin and his infamous Camelot. The castle was constructed to resemble the court where it's believed King Arthur reigned for so many years. *(Cornwall)*

I-SPY points: 25

Date: _____

Battles on British soil are generally grouped into six categories:

ANGLO-SAXON WARS

MEDIEVAL WARS

WARS OF THE ROSES

SCOTTISH WARS

CIVIL WAR

STUART UPRISING

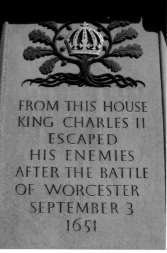

FROM THIS HOUSE
KING CHARLES II
ESCAPED
HIS ENEMIES
AFTER THE BATTLE
OF WORCESTER
SEPTEMBER 3
1651

Battle of Worcester Tablet

A full list of these significant battles appears on page 30 and details of some of the more infamous battles and battle sites can be found on pages 31-45.

I-SPY Tick List:

• **James IV (Scotland) 35** ◯

George II was the last British King to lead his army into battle.

1 Adwalton Moor	26 Newburn Ford
2 Barnet	27 Newbury
3 Blore Heath	28 Northallerton
4 Boroughbridge	29 Northampton
5 Bosworth Field	30 Otterburn
6 Braddock Down	31 Roundway Down
7 Chalgrove	32 Rowton Heath
8 Cheriton	33 Sedgemoor
9 Cropredy Bridge	34 Shrewsbury
10 Edgehill	34 Solway Moss
11 Evesham	36 Stamford Bridge
12 Flodden	37 Stoke Field
13 Halidon Hill	38 Stow-on-the-Wold
14 Hastings	39 Stratton
15 Homildon	40 Tewkesbury
16 Hopton Heath	41 Towton
17 Langport	42 Winceby
18 Lansdown Hill	43 Worcester with Powick
19 Lewes	Bridge
20 Maldon	
21 Marston Moor	
22 Myton	
23 Nantwich	
24 Naseby	**I-SPY points: 15,**
25 Nevill's Cross	for each site visited
	Date: _____

The arrival of the Roman Empire in AD43 was not so much of a battle as an invasion. Around 40,000 Roman troops landed at Richborough, Kent led by the Emperor Claudius. The invasion was neither quick nor painless. The anti-Roman campaign was led by Caratacus who was finally captured and taken to Rome. The campaign was taken on by Boudicca, queen of the Iceni, who was herself finally defeated by the Roman governor Suetonius Paulinus. The conquest was completed in AD75-77. By AD122 the Roman Empire had reached its most northerly point with the building of Hadrian's Wall – intended to keep the Pictish (Scottish) tribes out of Britannia.

I-SPY points: 25, for any reference to Roman invasion or empire

Date:_____

I-SPY points: 20, for Hadrian's Wall

Date:_____

THE BATTLE OF STAMFORD BRIDGE

September 25, 1066

The final battle in the long Viking raids. Norse resistance finally crumbled and the Vikings fled. Stamford Bridge was a great triumph for King Harold and the Saxons. But with their strength depleted the weary Saxons turned south to meet William the Conqueror at the fateful Battle of Hastings.

I-SPY points: 30

Date: _____

BATTLE OF HASTINGS

14 October 1066

1066 is the most memorable date in English history.

In a battle that lasted only one day, a group of Norman soldiers, led by William, Duke of Normandy defeated the English King Harold and won his kingdom. It took place at Senlac Hill, 10 km northwest of Hastings. William marched through Sussex and Kent crushing any resistance and had himself crowned King William I in Westminster Abbey on Christmas Day.

Most of the information on the events of that day comes from the Bayeux Tapestry. A copy of which is on exhibition in the Museum of Reading.

I-SPY points: 30

Date: _____

Bayeux Tapestry

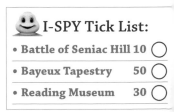

🙂 I-SPY Tick List:

• **Battle of Seniac Hill**	10 ◯
• **Bayeux Tapestry**	50 ◯
• **Reading Museum**	30 ◯

The Wars of the Roses was a dynastic struggle for the English throne fought between the two rival branches of the royal House of Plantagenet. Both houses contained the descendants of Edward III: the Duke of Lancaster and the Duke of York (the "red" and the "white" rose, respectively).

The final victory went to a relatively remote Lancastrian claimant, Henry Tudor, who defeated the last Yorkist king Richard III and married Edward IV's daughter Elizabeth of York to unite the two houses. The House of Tudor subsequently ruled England and Wales for 117 years.

I-SPY points: 30, for any connection to Edward III

Date: _____

I-SPY points: 30, for any connection to Richard III

Date: _____

The following are some of the key battles during the conflict.

THE BATTLE OF TOWTON

March 29, 1461

A terrible hand-to-hand battle in driving snow that lasted all day. Bodies piled high in the freezing cold and fresh troops had to climb over corpses to reach the front line. Yorkist reinforcements finally arrived and pushed the Lancastrians back, who broke and ran. At least as many perished in the panic that followed: the death toll reached 28,000. More men were killed at Towton than any other battle on British soil.

(Near Selby, North Yorkshire)

I-SPY points: 30

Date: _____

THE BATTLE OF BOSWORTH FIELD

May 4, 1471

The Lancastrians were fiercely pushed back when King Edward attacked the centre of their lines. Many drowned trying to escape. A terrible massacre followed and as many as 2,000 Lancastrians died. Edward, Prince of Wales the last legitimate descendant of Henry IV was killed. *(Near Market Bosworth, Leicestershire)*

I-SPY points: 30

Date: _____

THE BATTLE OF TEWKESBURY

August 22, 1485

King Richard III was defeated after his main ally Lord Stanley sided with Henry Tudor. Stanley's men joined Tudor's side and Richard's fate was sealed. Killed on the field, it is believed that Richard's crown was found on a bush and Henry Tudor placed it upon his own head. The Yorkists were finally defeated and Henry Tudor crowned Henry VII, starting the Tudor Dynasty, and a new era in English history

I-SPY points: 30

Date: _____

The Bishops' Wars 1639-1640

The Bishops' Wars were fought between the Scots and English forces led by Charles I, who wanted to reform the Scottish church. He was furious that Parliament rejected his proposals and when he discovered the Scots had been plotting with the French, mounted a military expedition. Parliament was against such an action – Charles I simply dismissed them. The battle was a disaster; the Scots seized Northumberland and Durham. Desperate for money, the king was forced to re-call Parliament in November 1640 (known as the "Long Parliament').

Durham Cathedral

I-SPY points: 30,
for any battle site of
The Bishops' Wars

Date:

I-SPY points: 30,
for Charles I

Date:

Civil war erupted in 1642 and was fought at every level of society throughout the British Isles. Charles I's men fought for traditional government in both church and state. The supporters of Parliament sought radical changes in religion and economic policy, plus a greater share of power at national level. The King officially began the war by raising his standard at Nottingham in August 1642. England was at war with itself.

I-SPY points: 30,
for any event relating
to the civil wars
Date: _____

Nottingham Castle

The following are key battles during the conflict.

THE BATTLE OF MARSTON MOOR

July 2, 1644

The Parliamentary army surprised the Royalists by attacking at dusk. Fierce fighting lasted for several hours: 6,000 were killed. Oliver Cromwell rose to power after defeating the Royalist cavalry. York was taken and the north of England was effectively lost to the King. *(Near Long Marston, North Yorkshire)*

I-SPY points: 30
Date: _____

THE BATTLE OF NASEBY

June 14, 1645

Cromwell's superior tactical manoeuvring and numbers began a total rout of royalists, chasing them 12 miles from Naseby; the king's army was captured and slaughtered. The King finally surrendered in Oxford in 1646. Oliver Cromwell was fully established as the Lord Protector of England and its sole ruler. *(Near Deventry, Northamptonshire)*

I-SPY points: 30
Date: _____

CIVIL WAR TIMELINE

1629   Charles I dissolves Parliament determined to govern without one.

1633   Archbishop Laud became Archbishop of Canterbury

1634-40   Ship Money Case

1637   Hampden's case supports Charles I's claim to collect Ship money – a tax applied to coastal towns to help pay for their defense.

1637-40   Breakdown of Charles's government of Scotland and two attempts to impose his will by force

1640   Long Parliament summoned

1641   Remodelling of the government in England and Scotland; abolition of conciliar courts.

1642   King Charles raised standard at Nottingham. The Battle of Edgehill (Indecisive).

1644   Battle of Marston Moor (Parliamentary Victory)

1645   Battle of Naseby (Parliamentary Victory)

1646   Charles I surrendered to Scottish Army.

1646   Oliver Cromwell established as Lord Protector

1648   Royalist and Presbyterian rising supressed by Cromwell and New Model Army.

1649   Charles I beheaded.

1649-50   Cromwell invaded Ireland

1650   Cromwell defeated Royalists under "King Charles II" at Dunbar, Scotland.

1651   Battle of Worcester, the last battle of the Civil War (Parliamentary Victory).

Scotland was an independent Kingdom and two wars (1296–1328) and (1332–1357) against the English saw Scotland retain its status as an independent nation.

THE BATTLE OF FLODDEN

September 9, 1513

The Scots were undone as much by their choice of weapon as by their opponents. The use of the long pike at close quarters was virtually useless. The resulting massacre saw King James and 5,000 of his men slain.

I-SPY points: 30

Date: _____

Wars of Scottish Independence I-SPY

The Stuart uprising saw battle between the troops of James Scott, Duke of Monmouth and his uncle James II, from whom he was attempting to seize the throne.

THE BATTLE OF SEDGEMOOR

July 6, 1685

Monmouth's plan was to attack under the cloak of silence. When a shot was fired over a mile out, the element of surprise was gone. Attacked on three sides, some 1,300 rebels were killed and another 500 were captured. Monmouth was captured and executed, his followers brutally suppressed by Judge Jeffries during their trials. So ferocious were the reprisals that Jeffries' court became known as the Bloody Assizes. *(Westonzoyland, Somerset)*

I-SPY points: 30

Date: _____

The church at Westonzoyland from the top of which the Battle of Sedgemoor was observed.

The Napoleonic Wars ran from 1803-1815 culminating with Napoleon's defeat in the Battle of Waterloo to an alliance of troops from the Great Britain, Russia, Prussia, Austria, the Netherlands and several German states. (see page 53) During the wars there was fear of a French invasion of Britain. Local fishermen from Hartlepool found, in the wreckage of a French warship, a ship's monkey, dressed in a military style uniform. Assuming this creature to be a French spy, they sentenced it to death by hanging from local gallows. (A popular story, but unlikely to be true.....).

I-SPY points: 30

Date: _____

Hartlepool Monkey

BATTLE OF TRAFALGAR

21 October 1805

A sea battle between Great Britain and the combined navies of France and Spain close to Cape Trafalgar in southwest Spain. The battle ended with a clear victory for the British navy.

Admiral Lord Nelson was mortally wounded during the battle and died on board HMS Victory. Trafalgar Square in London was named after the victory and the statue in the centre, Nelson's Column, commemorates the great naval war hero. He is laid to rest in St Paul's Cathedral, London.

I-SPY points: 30, for any connection to Nelson

Date: _____

A war fought between the Russian Empire and an alliance of the French Empire, the British Empire, the Ottoman Empire, and the Kingdom of Sardinia. The war was part of a long-running feud between the major European powers for influence over territories of the declining Ottoman Empire. Most of the conflict took place on the Crimean Peninsula. Florence Nightingale famously supported the wounded in the Crimea and earned the nickname 'the Lady with the Lamp'.

I-SPY points: 25, for Crimean Memorial

<u>Date:</u> _____

I-SPY points: 25, for Florence Nightingale Memorial

<u>Date:</u> _____

Florence Nightingale Memorial

Crimean Memoria

WORLD WAR I

The Great War was started by the assassination on 28th June 1914 of Archduke Franz Ferdinand of Austria. The resulting conflict caused the map of Europe to redrawn. The War ended on 11th November 1918 – subsequently known as Armistice Day.

I-SPY points: 20
Date:

WORLD WAR II

The global conflict of 1939-1945 involved most of the world's nations and was the most widespread war in history.

I-SPY points: 20
Date:

KOREAN WAR *(25 June 1950-27 July 1953)*

Korea had been ruled by Japan from 1910 to the end of World War II. It was then divided along the 38th parallel, the north ruled by Soviet troops, the south by United States troops. North Korean forces invaded South Korea on 25th June 1950 – the first (significant) armed conflict of the Cold War.

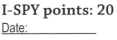

I-SPY points: 50
Date:

Stained glass window at St James Church, Sutton Cheney, Leicestershire depicting the Battle of Bosworth Field

One theme runs through all battles – that of survival – but victory can often come at a great price. The number of men involved and the number of lives lost in some of the biggest battles, is staggering (Battle of Towton ~ 1461 saw over 28,000 lose their lives – see page 34).

When the king led his troops into battle, he did it from the front.

King Harold was the last reigning monarch to suffer defeat by an invading force on British soil at the Battle of Hastings in 1066.

George II was the last British King to lead his army into battle, during the War of the Austrian Succession, at the Battle of Dettingen in Bavaria (now southwest Germany), 27th June, 1743.

The last English King to die in battle was Richard III at the Battle of Bosworth Field in Leicestershire on 22nd August 1485. Richard was defeated by Henry Tudor (later Henry VII), ending the Wars of the Roses between the Houses of York and Lancaster and starting the Tudor dynasty.

Flodden Field

The last Scottish King to die in battle was James IV of Scotland who was killed at the Battle of Flodden Field in Northumberland on 9th September 1513.

😊 I-SPY Tick List:		
• **King Harold**	25	◯
• **Battle of Hastings**	20	◯
• **George II**	30	◯
• **Richard III**	30	◯
• **Battle of Bosworth**	25	◯
• **Henry VII**	30	◯
• **Battle of Flodden Field**	35	◯

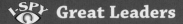

BOUDICCA
(1st century AD)
Queen of ancient Britain, Boudicca led a successful revolt against the Roman army that had claimed her deceased husband's kingdom.

I-SPY points: 40, for any connection to Boudicca
Date: _____

EDWARD III *(1312-1377)*
The long reign of Edward III saw the beginning of the Hundred Years' War with France. It started in 1338 with him claiming the French throne, but was also about opening trade routes in Europe. The outbreak of bubonic plague in 1348 saw half of England's population killed in two years. It was also a time of social reform: English replaced French as the official language and Parliament met regularly.

I-SPY points: 40, for any connection to Edward III
Date: _____

HENRY V *(1386-1422)*

A keen soldier, Henry V immediately renewed the Hundred Year's War with France. He won a great victory at Agincourt in 1415, which crippled France, led by the insane Charles VI. Following the Treaty of Troyes in 1420, Henry married Charles's daughter Catherine and his son was declared heir to both the English and French throne. He died suddenly in 1422, possibly from dysentery while campaigning in France.

I-SPY points: 40, for any connection to Henry V

Date: _____

RICHARD III
(1452-1485)

Richard III claimed the throne under suspicious circumstances following the imprisonment of his young nephews in the Tower of London. Although an able soldier and clever administrator, he was ruthless and deeply unpopular. He put down a rebellion by the Duke of Buckingham and was then killed at the decisive Battle of Bosworth Field in 1485, which put the Tudor Duke of Richmond in power and virtually ended the Wars of the Roses.

I-SPY points: 40, for any connection to Richard III

Date: _____

SIR FRANCIS DRAKE
(1540-1598)

Drake was an experienced seafarer and a favourite of Elizabeth I. He successfully circumnavigated the globe between 1577-1580 and was active in the battle against the Spanish Armada in 1588. He captured, without a single shot being fired, the Spanish flagship the Rosario, complete with the royal money chest.

I-SPY points: 40, for any connection to Drake

Date: _____

HENRY VII *(1457-1509)*

The Tudor dynasty began in bloodshed but heralded a more peaceful era. Henry restored order to the nation, introduced heavy taxes and fines and removed power from his squabbling nobles. He married Elizabeth of York, wed his eldest son Arthur (who died young) to Spanish princess Catherine of Aragon and his daughter Margaret to King James IV of Scotland, forming important political allies. Trade and exploration increased and national stability was restored.

I-SPY points: 40, for any connection to Henry VII

Date: _____

QUEEN ELIZABETH I
(1533-1603)

The last Tudor monarch inherited a country split by religious troubles; the French and Scots had allied and all English lands in France were lost. She was an exceptional woman, clever and crafty, and popular with her subjects. Her armies helped the Protestant cause throughout Europe and Scotland and she reinstated much of her father Henry VIII's legislation.

This caused friction with Spain, whose famous Armada was defeated in the English Channel in 1588. During Elizabeth's reign, great explorers sailed around the world, trade increased, William Shakespeare's plays were written and theatres built.

I-SPY points: 40, for any connection to Elizabeth I

Date: _____

OLIVER CROMWELL
(1599-1658)

A military and political leader who served as Lord Protector of England, Scotland and Ireland following the execution of King Charles I in 1649 and turned the country into a republican Commonwealth.

I-SPY points: 40, for any connection to Cromwell

Date: _____

DUKE OF WELLINGTON
(1769-1852)

Arthur Wellesley, 1st Duke of Wellington is often referred to as the 'Duke of Wellington' even though there have been subsequent Dukes. He rose to the position of Field-Marshall, commanded the allied army which defeated Napoleon at the Battle of Waterloo and was twice Prime Minster.

I-SPY points: 25, for any connection to Wellington

Date: _____

VICE ADMIRAL HORATIO NELSON
(1758-1805)

One of Britain's most heroic figures, Nelson was an officer who fought in a number of decisive naval victories, notably the Battle of Trafalgar in which he was fatally wounded.

I-SPY points: 40, for any connection to Nelson

Date: _____ ◯

SIR WINSTON CHURCHILL *(1874-1965)*

Winston Churchill is best remembered as the wartime leader who inspired and motivated the nation to victory in World War II. Born at Blenheim Palace in Oxfordshire, he is the only British Prime Minister to have been awarded the Nobel Prize for Literature and was the first person to be made an Honorary Citizen of the United States. He is buried at St Martin's Church, Bladon in Oxfordshire.

I-SPY points: 40, for any connection to Churchill

Date: _____ ◯

ANGLO-SAXON

Early battles were generally fought to repel invaders – particularly the Vikings. This warrior race came in great warships to take the country by force. Fighting was brutal: battle was hand-to-hand, each side forming a shield wall to attack. The main weapon was the spear. When shields clashed, rear ranks rained down with their heavy axes, inflicting savage blows to shield or limbs. Once the shield wall was fractured, the attacking troops were merciless in their slaughter.

By the time of the Battle of Hastings, the two-handed axe had been copied from the Vikings and was of standard use to the Anglo-Saxons.

I-SPY Tick List:

• **Viking Warship**	35	◯
• **Spear**	20	◯
• **Heavy Axe**	30	◯
• **Two-handed Axe**	30	◯
• **Shield**	25	◯

The Normans used the kite shaped shield to protect the warrior on horseback.

MEDIEVAL

Knights in battle began to wear full face helmets (helms), their shields adapted from the Norman kite shield (tear drop) with a flat top. Full plate armour was in widespread use and with it the large two handed sword. Archers were a common sight in the battlefield. Around this time the powerful longbow was used – a longbow could penetrate armour and shields within a 46m range.

😊 I-SPY Tick List:

• **Knight in Armour**	30	◯
• **Suit of Armour**	25	◯
• **Two-handed Sword**	25	◯
• **Archer**	30	◯
• **Longbow**	20	◯

WARS OF THE ROSES

Most soldiers were now fighting on foot with two-handed pole arms (pike) with an open faced sallet helmet to offer some protection. Topping the pole were protective metal strips; a variant was the bill, which held a nasty combination of hook, spike and blade. Another option was the pole-axe with a wide blade reversed with a hammer head. Knights were able to wear full suits of armour, interlocking with curved surfaces to deflect sword or arrows. Archers would carry small daggers that could be used to attack wounded knights, stabbing between the armour joints. Early cannons were first used, although their unreliability made them as dangerous to the gunners as to the enemy. So too were primitive handguns.

I-SPY Tick List:

• **Pike**	25	◯
• **Sallet Helmet**	25	◯
• **Pole-axe**	25	◯
• **Dagger**	20	◯
• **Early Cannon**	30	◯
• **Primitive Handgun**	30	◯

CIVIL WAR

Cavalry was more prominent in charges, the riders wearing "lobster" helmets with back and breastplate armour. Cannons became bigger and more reliable; cannon balls had devastating effects although they were heavy to move around and took a long time to reload. Handguns developed into muskets, firing lead musket balls, and pistols. Pike and bill formation attacks were still prevalent. Falconets (light cannons), were far more easy to reload and manoeuvre than the heavy great cannons. Muskets came with heavy butts, often used as a club when the ammunition ran out.

😊 I-SPY Tick List:

• **Lobster Helmet**	20	◯
• **Large Cannon**	25	◯
• **Cannon Ball**	20	◯
• **Musket**	25	◯
• **Falconet**	20	◯
• **Knight on Horseback**	25	◯

War memorials can be found in most towns and villages. National memorials such as the one commemorating the Battle of Britain in World War II are located in London.

I-SPY points: 10,
for a war memorial
Date: _____

I-SPY points: 25, for
Battle of Britain Memorial
Date: _____

Battle of Britain Memorial

NATIONAL ARMED FORCES MEMORIAL

A tribute to the men and women killed on active duty or as a result of terrorism since World War II.
(Alrewas, Staffordshire)

I-SPY points: 35
Date: _____

CENOTAPH

The Cenotaph, on Whitehall, is the county's official war memorial, commemorating servicemen and women who died in the two World Wars and is the centre of the Remembrance Day ceremony held on the Sunday closest to the 11th November each year.

I-SPY points: 15

Date: _____

UNKNOWN WARRIOR

Westminster Abbey's most moving memorial is the grave of the Unknown Warrior. Truly unknown, he was buried with the highest honours in 1921 and lies in soil brought from the battlefield: an anonymous representative of more than a million men who gave their lives in World War I.

I-SPY points: 20

Date: _____

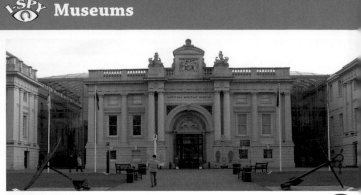

NATIONAL MARITIME MUSEUM

The National Maritime Museum displays an unrivalled collection of maritime artefacts. *(London)*

I-SPY points: 20

Date: _____

IMPERIAL WAR MUSEUM

The Imperial War Museum tells the story of British military conflicts from World War I to the present day. *(London)*

I-SPY points: 20

Date: _____

IWM DUXFORD

The Duxford branch of the Imperial War Museum is Britain's largest aviation museum with nearly 200 exhibits in seven main buildings. The original hangars, used in the Battle of Britain are still in use today. *(Cambridgeshire)*

I-SPY points: 20
Date: _____

TANK MUSEUM

The Tank Museum houses what is believed to be the finest collection of tanks and armoured vehicles in the world; from the very first British tank of 1915 up to Britain's latest battle tank – Challenger 2. Here you can learn why tanks were invented, how they work and what it was like to be a member of the crew. *(Bovington, Dorset)*

I-SPY points: 20
Date: _____

RAF MUSEUM

The history of aviation and the Royal Air Force is centred on two museums – the Royal Air Force Museum London and the Royal Air Force Museum Cosford in the West Midlands.

RAF Hendon

I-SPY points: 25,
for either

Date: _____

NATIONAL ARMY MUSEUM

Located next to the Royal Hospital Chelsea (home to the Chelsea Pensioners), the National Army Museum shows the history of the British Army over five floors of exhibits. *(Chelsea, London)*

I-SPY points: 20

Date: _____

Index

Aberystwyth Castle	16	Cromwell, Oliver	52	Ludlow Castle	26
Adwalton Moor	30	Cropredy Bridge	30	Maldon	30
Alnwick Castle	23	Dagger	56	Marston Moor	30
Archer	55	Denbigh Castle	17	Moat	8
Arrow Loopholes	7, 15	Dover Castle	11, 19	Motte	14
Arundel Castle	22	Drake, Sir Francis	50	Motte and Bailey Castle	4
Bailey	14	Drawbridge	12	Murder Hole	10
Bamburgh Castle	3	Dungeon	9	Musket	57
Barbican	12	Durham Cathedral	36	Myton	30
Barnet	30	Early Cannon	56	Nantwich	30
Battle of Bosworth Field	35, 46	Edgehill	30	Naseby	30
Battle of Britain Memorial	58	Edinburgh Castle	9, 11, 18	National Armed Forces Memorial	58
Battle of Dettingen	46	Edward I	16	National Army Museum	62
Battle of Flodden	40	Edward III	33, 48	National Maritime Museum	60
Battle of Hastings	32	Elizabeth I	51	Nelson, Vice Admiral Horatio	43, 53
Battle of Marston Moor	38	Evesham	30	Nevill's Cross	30
Battle of Naseby	38	Falconet	57	Newburn Ford	30
Battle of Sedgemoor	41	Flint Castle	16	Newbury	30
Battle of Stamford Bridge	32	Flodden	30	Nightingale, Florence	44
Battle of Tewkesbury	35	George II	29, 46	Northallerton	30
Battle of Towton	34	Goodrich Castle	26	Northampton	30
Battle of Trafalgar	43	Great Hall	11	Nottingham Castle	37
Battle of Worcester	29	Hadrian's Wall	31	Old Sarum	5
Battlements	13	Halidon Hill	30	Otterburn	30
Beaumaris Castle	16	Handgun	56	Pike	56
Blore Heath	30	Harlech Castle	16	Pole-axe	56
Bodiam Castle	19	Harold	47	Portcullis	13
Boroughbridge	30	Hartlepool	42	RAF Museum	62
Bosworth Field	30	Hastings	30	Restormel Castle	27
Boudicca	48	Hawarden Castle	17	Rhuddlan Castle	16
Braddock Down	30	Heavy Axe	54	Richard III	33, 47, 49
Builth Castle	16	Henry VII	46, 51	Rochester Castle	24
Caernarfon Castle	14, 16, 24	Henry V	49	Roundway Down	30
Cannon	57	Hever Castle	8, 12, 23	Rowton Heath	30
Cannon Ball	57	Holt Castle	17	Ruthin Castle	16
Cardiff Castle	8	Homildon	30	Sallet Helmet	56
Carlisle Castle	13, 20	Hope Castle	16	Sedgemoor	30
Castle Howard	21	Hopton Heath	30	Shield	54
Castle Wiston	4	Imperial War Museum	60	Shrewsbury	30
Cenotaph	59	Imperial War Museum, Duxford	61	Solway Moss	30
Chalgrove	30	James IV	29	Spear	54
Charles I	36	Judge Jeffries	41	Stamford Bridge	30
Cheriton	30	Kenilworth Castle	27	Sterling Castle	11
Chirk Castle	17	Knight in Armour	55	Stoke Field	30
Churchill, Sir Winston	53	Knight on Horseback	57	Stow-on-the-Wold	30
Colchester Castle	5	Korean War	45	Stratton	30
Conway Castle	16	Langport	30	Suit of Armour	55
Corfe Castle	28	Lansdown Hill	30	Tank Museum	61
Crenulations	13	Leeds Castle	22	Tewkesbury	30
Crimean Memorial	44	Lewes	30	Tintagel Castle	28
		Lincoln Castle	21	Tower of London	25
		Lobster Helmet	57	Towton	30
		Longbow	55	Two-handed Axe	54
				Two-handed Sword	55
				Unknown Warrior	59
				Viking Warship	54
				War Memorial	58
				Warwick Castle	9, 18
				Wellesley, Arthur	52
				Wellington, Duke of	52
				Westminster Abbey	59
				William the Conqueror	25
				Winceby	30
				Windsor Castle	20
				Worcester	30
				World War I	45
				World War II	45
				Yelden Castle	14

First published by Michelin Maps and Guides 2012 © Michelin, Proprietaires-Editeurs 2012. Michelin and the Michelin Man are registered Trademarks of Michelin. Created and produced by Blue Sky Publishing Limited. All rights reserved. No part of this publication may be reproduced, copied or transmitted in any form without the prior consent of the publisher. Print services by FingerPrint International Book production – fingerprint@pandora.be. The publisher gratefully acknowledges the contribution of the I-Spy team: Camilla Lovell, Geoff Watts and Ruth Neilson in the production of this title. The publisher gratefully acknowledges the contribution of Julian McKinlay, Jeffrey L. Thomas, The Tank Museum, RAF Museum, IWM Duxford, Players Cigarette Cards - National Portrait Gallery, Britain on View, Robin Sayer, Neil Holmes, Paul Lewis, and Unitaw Limited who provided the photographs in this book. Artwork by KJA-Artists. Other images in the public domain and used under a creative commons licence. All logos, images, designs and image rights are © the copyright holders and are used with kind thanks and permission. 10 9 8 7 6 5 4 3 2 1

I-SPY

One Token

7174894

HOW TO GET YOUR I-SPY CERTIFICATE AND BADGE

Every time you score 1000 points or more in an I-Spy book, you can apply for a certificate

HERE'S WHAT TO DO, STEP BY STEP:

Certificate

- Ask an adult to check your score
- Ask his or her permission to apply for a certificate
- Apply online to www.ispymichelin.com
- Enter your name and address and the completed title
- We will send you back via e mail your certificate for the title

Badge

- Each I-Spy title has a cut out (page corner) token at the back of the book
- Collect five tokens from different I-Spy titles
- Put Second Class Stamps on two strong envelopes
- Write your own address on one envelope and put a £1 coin inside it (for protection). Fold, but do not seal the envelope, and place it inside the second envelope
- Write the following address on the second envelope, seal it carefully and post to:

I-Spy Books
Michelin Maps and Guides
Hannay House
39 Clarendon Road
Watford
WD17 1JA